JOHN SIDDIQUE
Don't Wear It On Your Head,
Don't Stick It Down Your Pants

JOHN SIDDIQUE is a Poet who was born in the
North of England, He likes good stories, and he
likes meeting people who are individuals, he loves
salty & sour foods, he can't live without music. He
works both in the UK and abroad, reading, talking about and teaching poetry. He works a great
deal with schools and young people of all types,
and he has had many residencies and commissions
all over the world. His poems have appeared in
loads of anthologies and magazines. He currently
lives in West Yorkshire.

Also by John Siddique

FOR CHILDREN:
Don't Wear It On Your Head, Don't Stick It Down Your Pants (Salt)

FOR ADULTS:
Recital — An Almanac (Salt)
Blacpool — A Poet's View (Blackpool Council)
Poems from a Northern Soul (Crocus)
The Prize (Rialto)
Four Fathers (John is co-author of this book of stories) (Route)

www.johnsiddique.co.uk

Children's website at www.johnsiddique.co.uk/kids

Follow me at http://twitter.com/johnsiddique

JOHN SIDDIQUE

Don't Wear It On Your Head, Don't Stick It Down Your Pants

Poems for Young People

❖

CHILDREN'S POETRY LIBRARY
No. 5

SALT

LONDON

PUBLISHED BY SALT PUBLISHING
12 Norwich Road, Cromer,
Norfolk NR27 0AX United Kingdom

© John Siddique, 2006, 2010

First published by Inscribe 2006
This revised edition 2010
Reprinted 2013

Printed in the UK by TJ International Ltd, Padstow, Cornwall

Typeset in Oneleigh 11/14

ISBN 978 1 84471 763 7 paperback

3 5 7 9 8 6 4 2

For A.J. Rose, Simon, Ffion & Euan

CONTENTS

A WORD FROM THE POET

Hello

It's a good word isn't?

Thanks, is another good word, so thank you for reading my book. I am very proud of it especially the poem with the underpants in. I am very fond all of these poems because they were all written for young people in schools. A lot of them have great memories attached to them; of time spent in schools all over the country, laughing my socks off and getting help from young people with many of the details which help make the poems live.

Poetry thrives in schools. It is one of the most important places for poetry, which nearly all children seem to like at your age. I don't know what happens later to make people go off poetry, so that's where I come in, I try to keep poetry fresh and alive, as it is one of the most wonderful living parts of our language. It paints pictures deep inside us where other ways of using words can't go. So YEAH for poetry! YEAH to you for picking this book up! I hope I can show you some things, which excite you and make you want to have fun with language, make you want to value the amazing tool of words and communication.

Thanks
JOHN SIDDIQUE

Don't Wear It On Your Head, Don't Stick It Down Your Pants

'All I want of you
is that you shall achieve your own beauty
as the flowers do.'

—D.H. LAWRENCE

WHICH WAY ROUND IS THE TRUTH

The child that makes the parents.
The night that makes the day.
The cloud that makes the sky.
The marbles that make the play.

The skin that makes the colour.
The dark that makes the light.
The moon that makes the sun.
The wrong that makes the right.

The flight that makes the bird.
The poem that makes the life.
The cold that makes the heat.
The song that makes the words.

LOVELY DAY

It's a beautiful day
We go out to run
Lift up our arms, say YEAH
Lift up our faces to the sun
It feels like we're on holiday
We've only just begun
It's a beautiful day

MOON INSOMNIA

I eyed the moon right in the eyeball,
faced her face straight on in her fullness.
Her full face makes the tide flow.
Her full face makes the seeds under the soil
crack and split and root and grow.

I eyed the moon to see what she was saying.
My mouth shaping the words like her mouth,
she isn't saying anything, she has a dark side.
Her full face makes shapes become gargoyles,
squint and stare and try to imagine.

I eyed the moon until I could not sleep.
Face full of her, head full of her.
Her full face makes my mind glow.
Her full face heats my thoughts like oil,
rainbows, moonbows, where did the night go?

HEAD

Two eyes
Two ears
One nose
One mouth
One skin
One head
Same as everyone else

Two eyes
Two ears
One nose
One mouth
One skin
One head
Different from everyone else

SNOWFALL

It snowed last Christmas day where I live,
so we went up the hill opposite
while everyone else sat inside
with their grannies and their uncles,
and the red lipstick wearing aunties
who give scary red kisses. Everyone was eating,
and talking, and eating and steaming up their
windows. Repeating little worlds of families
from house to house to house.

We went up the hill in the snow,
there was no sound, everyone's inside.
Those without families were doing what they do,
even the silence of alone seems noisy.

The snow makes it all quiet.
Away from the windows, away from the dinner,
there is a blanket over the earth, the air is scrubbed
clean, and nothing is moving.

I wish it would snow for a year, and the telly breaks.
Then the radio goes off, and we forget to talk,
and we get a year of this crispy breathing quiet.

INSIDE IN

We wear skin all over our bodies,
on our heads and on our feet,
on our hands, and on our backs.
We have skin to keep our insides in.

We sun our skin, and soap our skin,
perfume it and stroke the cat with it.
Sometimes its itchy, sometimes it gets sore.
We need our skin to keep our insides in.

Some people don't like their skins
they say it makes them look too fat,
but really it's the fat that does that.
Some people try to change their skins
from white to brown, or brown to white,
pink to pale so that others might like them.

Some people don't like their skin
they say it makes them look too thin,
but really its being skinny that does that.
Some people love their skins, they scrub it,
steam it, oil it, cream it, tan it, shave it,
cover it, so that they can like themselves.

Skin lets the world come in. Nerve endings
bustling with life. Hot in the sun, wet in the rain,
the grain of the wood, a splinter OW! PAIN.
The touch of a face, holding a hand. Skin, skin,
it wraps around our lives to keep our insides in.

APPLES

A cold apple from the dish.
Crunch through its green.
Juice runs sweetly and sourly
in my mouth and down my chin.
Fingers grow sticky, I lick them clean.

NOSTRIL

I love the word nostril,
I say it many ways.
I have even been known to sing it
to the sound of Beethoven's 5th symphony.

I love what nostrils do,
breathe in the air, provide bogies to dig for,
but best of all they let you smell.

Smell the breakfast cooking.
Smell the petrol at the garage.
Smell the tar as they fix the road.
Smell the memories in burning wood.

FAMILY

We were not born under the same roof,
Not made from the same gene pool.
We don't like the same things,
don't think the same way.
We argue, and talk, and talk.
It's simply as complicated as this:
we are family.

WRONG DAY

I dipped the baby in the bath
to make sure the water wasn't too hot,
so I wouldn't burn my elbow.

It was midnight,
the sun was blazing down,
I put on my jumper.

On the empty hillside there were a million trees
I sat down and made a sandwich
from leaves and stones. It was lovely.

Poured myself
a nice hat of tea
from a chocolate teapot.

It got really dark
so I turned out the light
to see where I was going.

It was raining cows and bats,
so I put on my shoes
and went for a swim.

Woke up with a finish,
looked at my sundial,
it was early
I should be going home.

I took the express pig,
it goes round all the houses,
But the pig got a flat tyre,
so I fixed it with my trouser leg.

As I walked up the garden
I noticed the carpet needed mowing,
and that the cheese was still
drying on the line.

Yesterday will be better
I'm sure it will,
tomorrow was just too weird,
these days can make you fat.

CAT & MAT

The cat sat on the chair.
The cat sat on the table.
The cat sat in between the plants
on the windowsill.

The cat sat on the newspaper.
The cat sat on the cushion.
The cat sat on the shelf watching
my goldfish swimming.

What about the mat?
The cat and the mat?
We haven't got a mat,
we've got a wooden floor.

OUR TOWN

Our town is a grainy film.
Our town is busy.
Our town is red and black.
Our town is yellow and brown.

Our town is packed, busy,
chocka, rammed, stuffed,
swelling, blocked, mad,
restless, humming, rushed,
full to the brim,
crowded, bustling, INSANE
on Sunday and Saturday.

Our town is full of empty houses
during the week.

In our town everyone talks to everyone,
it can sometimes take an hour to
get along the street.

Our town is full of talkers.
Our town is full of plans.

LOVE

I will be the friend who will always see you right,
tell you I love you, even if you're being a twit.

I will hold your heart when its been ripped out.
I whisper to you to help the days move along.

I will leave kisses on your pillow.
I will wipe the blood from your hands
when you have fallen hard.

Sometimes I'm a fool and I don't help
you like I should.
Sometimes I'm just not enough.

Sometimes you just don't understand
that love is a two way thing,
I try to take up any slack.

Like a bud, becomes blossom, becomes seed.
Like chocolate only I don't make you fat.
I'm a midnight feast, a rustling duvet, a solid fact.
I keep on trying for you, to give you what you need.

DINNER LADIES

Dinner ladies stand with their hands on their hips.
Dinner ladies serve pizza, beans, soggy broccoli
    and chips, chips, chips.
They shout "Oi" really loud, and smash the mash
    on your plate.
They make you eat peas, sprouts and sweetcorn,
banana wots mushy, rice pudding as slushy as baby
    food.

Posh dinner ladies call themselves lunchtime
    supervisors,
they send you to the head-teacher for running on
    the grass.
Yell at you to get off the rails, and sometimes
they call you honey bunny in front of your mates.

HABITUAL FAMILY LIST

My mum swears when she tells me not to swear.
She always talks with her mouth full.

She dances to rock music, she is 78,
and she cannot help complaining about the cat.

Mum cries at anything sad on the telly,
never listens properly when you speak to her.

Only watches the news headlines.
Loves roast lamb the best.

Mum can save money
even when there isn't any.

She will always share anything she has,
no visitor will ever go hungry.

She turns off her phone when
she's watching Coronation Street.

HEYBROOK STREAM WHERE I USED TO PLAY

Heybrook Stream writing its name as
it swerves underneath Entwistle Road.

Heybrook Stream waving a cold hand,
reaching out to grab hot legs.

Heybrook Stream touching, splashing
and gurgling over rocks.

Heybrook Stream drawing me close
"Come in, come in," it whispers.

Heybrook Stream catching leaves,
catching the wind, catching my head.
Reminding a boy once upon a Summer.

GOSSIP

I'm a game of Chinese whispers that can kill.
A ninja assassin poised like a spider outside
on your windowsill. I am the poison that
makes the bully strong. That laughs
when you're hit in the face. That loves it when
your wrong.

I am the shoelace that is ready to snap
when you are already late for your friends.
I am a cold wind.
I wait by the lockers and in the playground.
I steal away friends. *Well you we're never good*
enough anyway.

Tonight I love you. Tomorrow I'll be telling stories
I'm the Prime Minister's smile — You know I'm a
       phoney.
I call at your house when you're out, tell your mum
I'm your friend; you were supposed to lend me
a book. I go through your drawer & steal your diary.

Then I graffiti your secrets in colours no one can
       refuse.
I speak quietly to get what I want, I'm always
       smiling.
What I want is your happiness.

BEDTIME

There's an owl that hoots every evening
from the trees behind our house.
It's gonna be a spooky night.
It's gonna be a spooky night.

The cupboard door makes dark dark shadows,
I want my mum.
It's a spooky night.
It's a spooky night.
Mummy!

I got a whoopee cushion free with my comic,
I put it on granddad's chair.
It's gonna be a trumpy night.
A loud trumpy night.

I ate too many beans before bed.
For lunch I had mushy peas.
It's going to be a trumpy night.
A well smelly night.
A blame the cat night.
It's going to be a trumpy night.

It's time for bed
I'm scared now and full of wind,
Dad tucks me up tight
for a sleepy night.
For a sleepy night.

I try to listen to his stories,
I can feel him warm beside me.
My eyes shut tight,
for a sleepy night.
A long sleepy night.

POET

Word dancer
Story teller
Rhythm shifter
Moon lover
Night walker
Day dreamer
Truth teller
Syllable stretcher
Soul painter
Life enhancer

SHOPPING DAY

We go shopping, Grandma, Dad, Mum and me.
Trolley wheels rattling, people nattering and
    chattering.
Walking down the aisles, smelling freshly baked
    bread.
Past the red, white and yellow flowers to buy fruit
    and veg.

Carrots, cucumber and cabbage.
2 kilos of apples, apricots and avocados too.
Radishes, raspberries and rhubarb.
Melons, mangoes, lemons and limes.
Barbecuing chickens make me hold my nose.
Got the fruit and veg, now we're moving on.

The raw fish on the ice look at us,
a whole chicken and some chorizo sausage,
pork chops, lamb chops, spare ribs.
Slices of beef and bacon, ham and turkey too.
Stickiness under our shoes from a broken jar
of marmalade. An announcement comes over
the speakers. *A cleaner to aisle 12 please.*

Dragged along the sweet aisle, liquorice reels,
    Haribos,
kali and Crunchies. Then along to get some cereal,

bran flakes and Coco Pops, Honey Nut Loops and
    Frosties.
Cookie Crisps, Wheetos, chocolate squares.

Running around for things we've forgotten.
Looking for baby food and wipes.
Tins of tuna, salmon and pilchards.
Pepper, toothpaste, shampoo and toilet roll.

We go shopping, Grandma, Dad, Mum and me.
Checkouts bleeping, carrier bags rustling,
money rattling in the till.

HEAD FOR TOMORROW

Tomorrow
I want to learn
what makes the clock of my mind
tick so loudly?

Why do someone else's chips
always taste better?

Why do noses itch so much
when you have to stand still in assembly,
or when you meet someone important?

Does my mind control my body?
Or my body control my mind?

Why are some friends real friends
and others are just people?

I want to know how we will live
if we kill our world?

I want to know what happens next.

MY OWN TEACHER

Teach me to be strong for myself,
I always need telling, even though,
I've shown myself many times already.

Teach me how one and one is not always two.

Teach me how to be the me I am,
and the me you want me to be at the same
        time.

Teach me the equations of the sunrise,
The maths of my mum's face,
The geography of wanting too much,
The history of the future.

Teach me to be strong enough to be gentle,
I make shapes in my mind, pictures of how it
        should be,
teach me to look through my eyes instead of
        the pictures.

GROWING PAINS

My legs ache at night.
The room feels too hot.
I need a drink of water.
Mum says, GET BACK TO BED.
I like to keep the light on.
I'm afraid of closed doors.
I'm thirsty, I want a biscuit.
My fingers creak and hurt.
I've got a headache.
I'm bored with my book.
I like to cuddle the cats.
It must be nearly time to get up.
Snore Zzzzzzzzzzz!

MAKING IT UP

Fold yourself the mind you want. Make a paper
hat and wear it on your head. Hold it tight
when the wind blows.

Paint yourself the heart you desire. Pin it
on your jumper, be proud of your colours.
Pin it fast and don't mind the rain.

Write yourself the love you love. Hold that
paper tight in your hand. Unfold it often,
read your plan aloud in sun and in snow.

Walk yourself the world you want. Each step
is breath. It's your life. Stamp big-footed.
Walk soft. Dance your way in all the weathers.

DON'T WEAR IT ON YR HEAD, DON'T STICK IT DOWN YR PANTS

I'm not sure if this is a poem,
not sure if it's just a list.
There is no philosophical content,
it could easily be dismissed.
But I will stand my ground and tell you
this is the truth,
be careful, really careful,
with what you wear as a hat,
with what you stick down your pants.

Don't wear it on yr head.
Don't stick it down yr pants.

A 52 inch plasma screen.
A 2-litre tub of vanilla ice cream.
A six-pack of coke.
A circus of fleas.
A hive of bees.
Your grandma's tartan shopping trolley.
An industrial size can of baked beans.
And cheese, don't do it, especially Dairylea.

Don't wear it on yr head.
Don't stick it down yr pants.

All the presidents of the USA,
or their mums and dads.
All of your loves.
All of your worries.
All of your lusts.
All of your fears.
All of your hates.
All of your mates,
and WH smiths.

Don't wear it on yr head.
Don't stick it down yr pants.

Confusion.
A rucksack.
A Porsche 928.
A note from your true love.
A train arriving late.
Your father's silence.
Your mother's questions.
All the things you never had.

Don't wear it on yr head.
Don't stick it down yr pants.

Buckingham palace.
The queen and her dogs.
A fox hunt,
or politics.
All the World's religions.
A notice of eviction.
A pint of contradiction.
A judge's jurisdiction.

Don't wear it on yr head.
Don't stick it down yr pants.

A racist.
A bully.
Someone else's ideas.
A treacle pudding.
A length of rope.
A mountain bike.
Your school report.

Don't wear it on yr head.
Don't stick it down yr pants.

A SMALL POEM CALLED VENGE-ANCE

Vengeance falling through my blood and veins,
but I do nothing at all.

Vengeance whispering in my head into flames,
pleading to be let out, for me to say its name.

Vengeance shooting, my mouth shouting,
stomach clenching, my fist ready to punch.

My fist flying in vengeance, harder, faster
than the speed of light.

TEACHER

Knowledge store
Tired being
Life shaper
Ability finder
Loud voice
Mind maker
Lion tamer
Surrogate mum

IN OUR FAMILY

The cats get fat, while we argue and fight
about the telly, biscuits, drinks.

In our family the rules change everyday
from black to white and back.

No one talks, or rather no one listens.
The dog is everyone's friend.

Food is the same on each day of the week,
Monday is pizza, Tuesday is beans . . .

This house is too small for all our noise
& the neighbours think we're mad.

& we are. Crazier than a reptile house
being overrun by chimps.

The house is not that clean, we never
help at all. We have sticky souls in our
    family.

A POEM FOR THE PEOPLE WHO TAUGHT ME

I have a blue cardboard box,
it was given to me by Amanda.
I keep all my treasure in that box.

I keep all my letters from my friends,
they teach me about being there for them.
They show me that they are there for me.

I keep, my old dog's lead,
Terry was his name.
Dogs love you no matter what.

I have a big brain.
It is like a chest of drawers,
stuffed full of poems and ideas.

Mum taught me to be myself
and let my poems come out.

Marie taught me to like my own skin,
to feel lovely in the sun.

Amanda taught me how to dance,
to jiggle my bits and shake my bones.

Chris taught me that he is my brother
even though we are not related.

And my other Chris
taught me that God is for me too,
in all the little things I do.
She taught me to be reliable,
and not to eat beans before bed.

HAIKUS OF THE SEASONS

Summer sun burning
Sunglasses and hot hot skin
— we dream of ice-cream

One red leaf spins down
Where has the year gone already?
The dark comes closer

Hot days in winter
Seasons are falling apart
— pollution warning

Daffodils brighten
We come out into the world
like it's the first time

HELPING OUT

Eating sugarcane in my uncle's field,
cut fresh with a machete.

Stringy strands between my teeth.
Sweet heaven in my mouth.

Wiping my chin with the back
of my hand before drenching myself
again with flowing sugar water.

MY BODY, MY MIND AND ME

From my head to my feet
I'm amazing.
From my bum to my tum
I'm amazing.
My body, my mind and me.

After school I like to run
Mum says be careful.
I run to feel the wind on my face.
The ground stamped by my feet.

After school
I watch the world go by.
My mates on the bus.
My neighbour's dog chasing her tail.

Lying on my belly in the garden
I smell the earth & the grass.
Wafting out the door, my tea
is cooking, mmmmmmm
chicken curry, my favourite.

The smack of a football.
The rumble of the river.
My sisters always squabbling,
I listen to them all.

Chocolate ice cream,
Salty, salty crisps, tickling my tongue
Mum says, you are what you eat,
that means I'm salty and sweet.
I think about horses.
Dream about seeing my granddad again.
Fill my head with ideas from books.
Where do ideas grow? How are they fed?
They live in all the talking, smelling, tasting,
seeing, hearing, touching
that I'll do until I'm dead.

From my head to my feet
I'm amazing.
From my bum to my tum
I'm amazing.
My body, my mind and me.

RAGE THINKS ABOUT ITSELF

Rage would like to be a flower bursting open,
pink and new, in a field that's just been mowed.

Rage wants to be a small King Charles puppy,
going round and round in a circle chasing its tail.

Rage thinks of being a collared dove, swirling
and twirling through the sky, away from its enemy.

INSIDE THE SHELL

I put the shell to my ear.
The sea rippling around,
roaring like a jet engine.

Inside the shell a tropical beach,
sand and seaweed, a silvering storm.

Sand man coming up from the sand.
Taller, taller, taller than me.
Singing his sand song to the wind,
and the thunder god.

SKANDA KARTIKEYA

War rides in to town as a peacock.
all his eyes on fire. Oil mixing with rain.

Peacock says: *This is my land.*
This is my oil. *This is my food.*

Fascinated, hypnotised, we stand & fall in love,
with the blue flaming fire of the bird.
His colours brighter than an Asian wedding.
We cover our ears at his siren of a cry,
It does not stop his voice.

A small boy, all ribs & arms & legs kills the bird
by turning his back on it.
Tonight we share bread and feast.

NOTE: Skanda Kartikeya is the Hindu god of war, who takes
the form of a peacock.

SNOW, RAIN, AND SUN

Snow don't blow
Snow don't grow
Snow just snows
Don't ya know?

Rain can't swim
It collects in tins
Plays drums on bins
It does, you know?

Sun don't love
Sun don't hate
It doesn't turn up late
EVER.

MEMORY PHOTO #1

It's lunchtime. The smell of burnt toast fills the room. Mum is by the cooker making a pot of tea. She looks tiny today. The sun streams in and lights up the smoky air. It is too warm to play in the garden. The dog is flat out asleep.

MEMORY PHOTO #2

I'm outside in the garden. I like to climb on top of the shed; up here things are more at my level. They can't find me so easily. The roof is full of bird pooh and small stones. I lean back against the hot brick wall. My back sweats and flexes.

MEMORY PHOTO #3

Fast down the hill on my bike, the ground turns white I'm moving so fast, will never make it round the corner, cannot put the breaks on, I'll die, Sean is far away behind me, I'm going to win. The pedal catches the pavement but I don't come off. Pedal, John, come on.

MONSOON SEASON

A sudden storm breaks the heat.
We've been sweating for days, unable to move.
Clothes sticking to skin.
Now the rain drops like marbles around my feet.

My dad is very set in his ways. *Do what your told,*
don't answer back. He raises his slipper and I run.
I try to make the beds, fetch the water
from the metal pump in the courtyard.

His grumpiness lifts when the rain comes down.
Boom goes the thunder. WHACK! FLASH!
Thunder and lightning. The burnt soil swirls
into mud. The green is coming. The air is cool.
We hold hands and dance soaked to the skin.

BORN HERE

Dad cooks pakora.
Mum fries bacon & eggs.

Dad turns to The East.
Mother makes the sign of the cross.

The playground leaves me out of its games,
tells me I don't belong here.
I stamp my feet and say *I do.*

My heart speaks in three languages,
Mum's, dad's and mine,
it says *I am the future.*

UNEXPECTED GUESTS

Put the door on the snib,
when there's a knock say *come in*.
The world is just a village,
come in, come in.

Put the world on the latch
when there's a knock say come in.
I'll cook you some lamb, or fish 'n' chips,
or plantain, or breadfruit or okra and potatoes.
Come in, come in.

Leave the country ajar,
please come in, have a seat.
We'll swap stories, and cry and laugh.
Shake hands. Eat something sweet:
Chocolate, gulab jamun, peanut butter cups
and rice pudding.
Do come in, come in.

The world is just a village
Put the door on the snib,
tell me a story,
come in, come in.

POETRY EXTRA

Here we are at the end of the book, and I thought it might be interesting to answer some of the questions I am always being asked in schools here, and I also thought I might show you a couple of things so that you can become a good poetry reader if you'd like to be, and few things to help you write better poems too.

I thought I'd do the questions first, I have been helped with the questions by Class 4 of Benjamin Hargreaves School in Lancashire, so these are real questions from real children.

How often do you write books?

I write almost every day, sometimes it's easy because I am at home, but often I am travelling to do poetry readings, or school visits and on those days I try my best. I keep a notebook and my favourite pen with me at all times, and I make notes of things I see and hear that interest me, or that I find beautiful.

Do you ever get stuck on words?

All the time, I didn't do very well at school so I have to work very hard sometimes to know what things mean. I have a lot of different types of dictionaries to help me find the words I need, or tell me their meanings.

How do you become a poet?

I know this is not a very good answer but it is the real one, you write poems! But more than that, you need to be interested in the world and its people, if you are you might find that you get pictures and words in your head in reaction to the things you see and hear, if you do then try writing them down. But not everyone can be a poet, some people are good at football, others art, or cooking or riding bikes or being a good friend, being creative comes out in many different ways so don't think that you must be able to be a poet.

Why did you want to be a poet?

I didn't, I was busy being a gardener then it snuck up on me. It was like poetry wanted me to be its friend, so it kept calling round for me and asking me to play with it. I am glad I became friends with it, as it is such a special thing in my life.

How long have you been a poet?

I wrote my first poem in 1993, you can do the maths from there.

What books do you like to read?

My five favourite poetry books for younger people at this time are:

> *Sensation* — edited by Roger McGough
> *The Works* — edited by Paul Cookson
> *The Puffin Book of Utterly Brilliant Poetry* — edited by Brian Patten
> *Can I Buy a Slice of Sky* — edited by Grace Nichols
> *The School Bag* — edited by Seamus Heaney and Ted Hughes

I love anthologies of poetry as you get to read lots of different poets; I also like to listen to poetry so I have some poetry cds that I listen to in the car.

I like reading all sorts of books; I really loved Philip Pullman's 'His Dark Materials,' books. I love myths and folk tales and especially creation myths.

What stories do you like to tell in your poetry?

I mostly write about people and how they get on with each other, but I also like to create worlds, which my readers' minds can explore as well, so I sometimes write mythic pieces. I like people who like to think about things, not puzzle them out, but who care and find it important to be thoughtful, respectful and com-passionate, so I try to create poems which help people see that it is okay to be these things.

How many books have you written?

This is my first book for young people; I hope you have enjoyed it. I write a lot for adults too, those books are very different from this one because of the way people's thinking changes as they grow up. I have published three books of poetry for adults, I am just writing a new one at the moment, and I'm writing a new kid's book too. I have also written short stories, and I am seriously thinking about writing some prose books of stories or a novel over the next few years.

Is it nice being a poet?

I love it, it's a strange job, not one I ever thought I'd have, but if you can find the thing you are supposed to be, then it doesn't feel like a job at all. I just feel so lucky to be around language, and that I get to travel and meet people of all sorts because of it.

JOHN'S TOP TIPS TO BE A GOOD POETRY READER

Get yourself a good anthology. I listed some in the interview preceding this bit, leave it somewhere in the house where you will keep coming across it. I have a bunch of anthologies next to the loo. Then try and read one poem each day.

Try reading aloud, either by yourself or with a friend, or one of your family. Reading poetry aloud lets you find a different way into the poem from reading it in your head. I find that reading together brings me closer to my friends and family. Also and this is a big secret so please don't share this ... Reading aloud is very good for improving your confidence in yourself. I used to be a very shy person, and over the years reading out loud has made me much more able to feel confident in being in the world.

Get a poetry readers group together at school, meet once a week and share your poetry finds with each other, work your way through a book, or select a poem each and discuss it with each other when you meet.

Get books as birthday and Christmas presents. Books are always great presents, make sure you have a bookshelf in your room and add a book to it when you can.

Make your own anthology: when you find a poem you like, copy it out into a scrapbook, and keep on adding poems to it to make your own anthology of favourite poems that are special to you.

HOW TO BE A POET

I could write a hundred books on this subject and it wouldn't be enough, but I'm going to try and say in one paragraph. In fact I'm just going to tell you the three secrets then if you want to have a go it's up to you.

Secret one: you know already, READ, to be able to write you have to read, this will show you what poems are and how they work, don't worry about whether poems rhyme of not. Look at how the story works in a poem. How the lines place pictures inside you. Read and read, and read.

Secret two: be interested in everything, and keep a notebook, if you feel interested in something make notes about it, stick pictures in your note book, draw pictures in it, mind maps, doodles, write down lines that come to you, reflect on the things you see, write down observations, collect words and ideas.

Secret three: don't wait to be inspired. When you want to write, just sit down and do it, don't worry about the quality, whether it's good or bad, and don't try to force the ideas to be like someone else's poem. Let it come out and enjoy the fact that sometimes its quick and easy, and sometimes its slow like fishing, and sometimes its really hard work. Copy other poets' styles have a go at every type of poem you can find, make your own forms up ... eventually your own style will come out.

Sounds simple doesn't it, it is and after years of being a writer I'm still doing all of these things, sometimes it works, sometimes it's not the time to write, I don't worry. There is no such thing as writers' block, sometimes it's the right time to write, other times it's time to be interested in things so that there is something to write about. If you feel like having ago there is one last secret, a really big one, **don't tell people your ideas before you've written your poem**. If you say it out loud before you write it down it will go away.

Thank you for reading my book, remember poems are for sharing — please tell other people about what you have enjoyed in this book.

Stay shiny
JOHN SIDDIQUE